We saw a stranger yesterday,
we put food in the eating place,
drink in the drinking place,
music in the listening place,
and with the sacred name of the triune god,
he blessed us and our house, our cattle and our dear ones,
as the lark says in her song,
often, often, often, goes christ in the stranger's guise.

Celtic rune of hospitality

GUESTS

IN CELEBRATION OF CELTIC HOSPITALITY

Co- published by:

Class 37   &   SCM-Canterbury Press Ltd,
Tiroran   St Mary's Works,
Isle of Mull   St Mary's Plain,
Argyll   Norwich
PA69 6ES   NR3 3BH
Tel. 01681 705 203   Tel. 01603 612914
e mail. fran@classthirtyseven.demon.co.uk   Fax. 01603 624483

©Photography by Martin Guppy.   with contribution by Nick Bonetti.

Design by Leigh Hurlock
tel. 01273 480 534

ISBN   1-853-356-5

Cover picture: Cottage Detail, Isle of Tiree.
Title page and back cover: Sunset over the Isle of Iona.

There is a door to which thou hast the key,
sole keeper thou.
There is a latch no hand can lift save thine.....
O heart make haste and bid him to thy hearth.
Nay urge him in....
So shalt thou win
joy such as lovers know when love is told,
peace that enricheth more than miser's gold.

Hebridean

hail guest, we know not whom thou art.
if friend, we greet thee hand and heart,
if stranger, such no longer be,
if foe, our love will conquer thee.

Copied from a Crofter's door..Wales

TOBERMORY, ISLE OF MULL.

MORE THINGS ARE LEARNT IN THE WOODS THAN FROM BOOKS.
ANIMALS, TREES AND ROCKS TEACH YOU THINGS
NOT TO BE HEARD ELSEWHERE.

St. Bernard

MAY THE BLESSING OF THE FIVE LOAVES AND THE TWO FISHES
WHICH GOD SHARED OUT AMONG THE FIVE THOUSAND BE OURS.
MAY THE KING WHO DID THE SHARING
BLESS OUR SHARING AND OUR PARTAKING.

An old Irish Grace

CORN STOOKS & CROFT, SOUTH UIST.

DATE	NAME & ADDRESS	COMMENT

Ⓜ**ay the earth be soft under you
when you rest out upon it,
tired at the end of the day:**

An Irish blessing

DATE	NAME & ADDRESS	COMMENT

The fosterage of my house,
is not of any common child;
Jesus with his heavenly company
shelters each night against my heart.

Source unknown

May the blessing of light be upon you,
light without and light within.
may the blessed sunlight shine upon you and warm your heart,
till it glows like a great peat fire,
so the stranger may come and warm himself at it,
and also a friend.

An Irish Blessing

The king is knocking.
if thou would'st have thy share of heaven on earth,
lift the latch and let in the king.

Hebridean.

The blessing of god upon this house.......
with plenty of food and plenty of drink,
with plenty of beds and plenty of ale,
with much riches and much cheer,
with many kin and length of life,
ever upon it.

From the Carmina Gaedelica

$\mathcal{B}$LESS TO US, O GOD,
THE MORNING SUN THAT IS ABOVE US,
THE GOOD EARTH THAT IS BENEATH US,
THE FRIENDS THAT ARE AROUND US,
YOUR IMAGE DEEP WITHIN US,
THE DAY WHICH IS BEFORE US.

St. Patrick

O KING OF STARS!
WHETHER MY HOUSE BE DARK OR BRIGHT,
NEVER SHALL IT BE CLOSED AGAINST ANY ONE,
LEST CHRIST CLOSE HIS HOUSE AGAINST ME.

From a Blessing for Hospitality

GRAZING HIGHLANDER, ISLE OF MULL.

If there be a guest in your house
and you conceal aught from him,
'tis not the guest that will be without it,
but Jesus, Mary's son.

From a Blessing for Hospitality

IONA VILLAGE GARDEN, LOOKING TOWARD THE SOUND OF IONA.

I wait with love's expectancy,
Lord Jesus trouble not to knock at my door.
My door is always on the latch.
Come in dear guest, and be my host and tell me all thy mind.

Ancient Gaelic

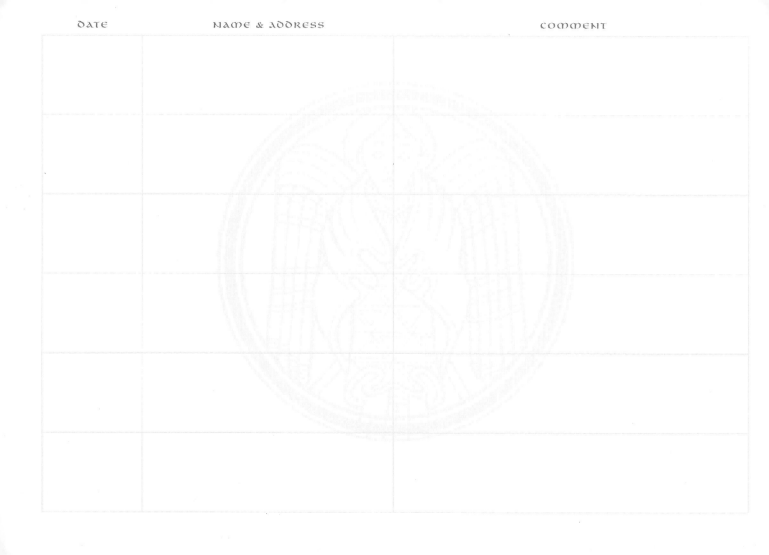

The sacred three,
my fortress be
encircling me,
come and be round
my hearth, my home.

From the Hebrides

IONA ABBEY CLOISTERS.

DATE	NAME & ADDRESS	COMMENT

Who stands on the grass outside?
Sun-bright Mary and her son,
The mouth of God requested, the angel of God spoke:
Angel's of promise guard the hearth
Until bright day visits the fire.

From a blessing on the fire at night

Do not neglect to show hospitality to strangers,
for thereby some have entertained angels unawares.

Hebrews 13:2 (rsv)